Nina felt as scared as a rabbit.
Her parents were splitting up.
She was going to stay with Mum.
Dad would live in another house.

4

Mum and Dad Love You

Written by Cecil Kim
Illustrated by Anna Ladecka
Edited by Joy Cowley

Nina heard some terrible news.
It was the worst thing
she had ever heard
in her entire life.
Mum and Dad were
getting a divorce.

6

Nina begged like a puppy.
"Mum, I'll be a good girl.
Dad, I'll study harder."

Mum said, "Nina, darling,
we are not splitting up
because of you."

Dad said, "It is because Mum
and I have decided
we will be happier living apart
than living together."

That night, Nina felt gloomy.
She felt like a bat in a dark cave.
So many worries filled her mind
she could not sleep.

8

9

The next day, Dad was packing.
Nina was like a naughty monkey.
She took Dad's things and hid them.
Then she pretended her finger hurt.

10

Dad said, "Nina, you and I will get to
spend time together on Saturdays.
We'll eat yummy food, and maybe
we'll even go on a trip somewhere."

Nina didn't answer.

As Dad left, he said,
"I will always love you, Nina."

Nina felt spiky like a porcupine.
"Lies!" she said. "All grown-ups are liars!"

14

Nina got very angry.

She hated her house.

She hated her mum.

She hated her homework.

She wouldn't eat.

She felt like an angry gorilla.

Then Nina saw her mother crying.
Mum didn't make a sound.
Her shoulders shook
and tears ran down her face.
Nina could not go to her.

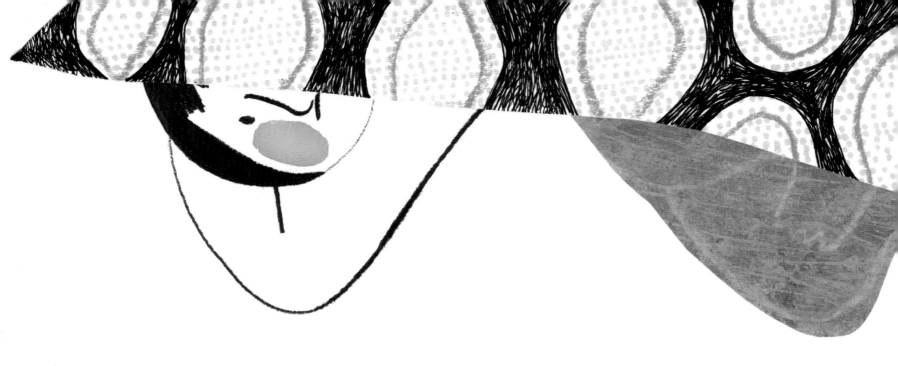

After that, Nina did not get angry.
She did not laugh.
She did not even talk.
She was like a turtle
in a hard shell.

Nina's teacher said to her,
"Nina, your mother told me
about the changes in your family.
I am so sorry. This must be
a hard time for you. It's okay
if you feel upset or sad. I understand."
Nina's teacher gave her a hug,
and Nina began to cry.
She opened her mouth like a hippo
and cried and cried.

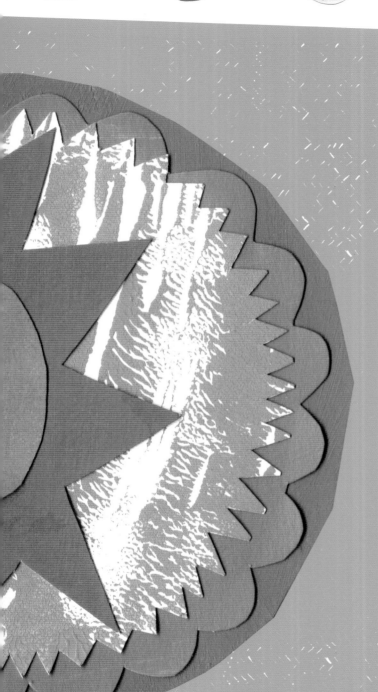

When Nina got home,
she gave her mum a hug.
Nina was like a cuddly bear.
She said, "It's okay, Mum."

Mum said, "Yes, Nina.
We're going to be okay."

At last it was Saturday.

Nina was very happy to see Dad.

They went to the zoo together.

She held his hand tightly.

She had been to the zoo before
with Mum and Dad.

Now it was just Dad
and that was okay.

She still had her mum and dad.
Their love for her had not changed.

24

Dearest Nina,

Dad and Mum are both very sorry that you are feeling so sad.
We want you to know that we both tried our best to keep our family together. We did everything we could think of to find a way to stay together and be happy. But nothing worked. So we decided that living apart from each other was the best choice for us. It was a hard decision to make, because we knew how much it would change your life. We love you so much that we did not want to make you feel pain or sadness.

We hope that as time goes by, the pain and sadness will heal for all of us. We know that all of these changes in our family will feel different at first, and it's okay to feel sad about that. Every new thing in life feels different at first. We believe that after a while these changes will start to feel normal and that we will all be okay. We also know one thing that will never ever change — our love for you!

With love from Mum and Dad

big & SMALL

Original Korean text by Cecil Kim
Illustrations by Anna Ladecka
Original Korean edition © Eenbook 2011

This English edition published by big & SMALL in 2016
by arrangement with Eenbook
English text edited by Joy Cowley
English edition © big & SMALL 2016

ISBN: 978-1-925234-47-3

Printed in Korea